Raising a smil

The Silvey-Jex Partnership

Published in the UK by
POWERFRESH Limited
21 Rothersthorpe Crescent
Northampton
NN4 8JD

Telephone 0845 130 4565
Facsimile 0845 130 4563
E Mail info@powerfresh.co.uk

Cover and interior layout by Powerfresh

ISBN 1902929756

Printed in Malta by Gutenberg Press limited
Powerfresh July 2003

AITER!! CAN I HAVE ANOTHER WIFE PLEASE
MINE'S FALLEN ON THE FLOOR

MEMBERS
ONLY
OLD
COMRADES
CLUB
NO DOGS.
SJ.

LOOK AT THESE PYJAMAS ALICE...
THERE'S A BIG RIP RIGHT WHERE...
...OH SORRY

DO YOU THINK SOMEONE SHOULD TELLHIM
IT'S OUT OF ORDER... HE'S BEEN STANDING
THERE HALF THE MORNING

7
DO NOT
DISTURB
S.J.

THAT WAS THE GREATEST BOOK I'VE EVER READ
... IT'S GOT REALLY BIG TYPE.

STEAK'S AS TOUGH AS HELL -
CAN'T GET MY TEETH INTO IT

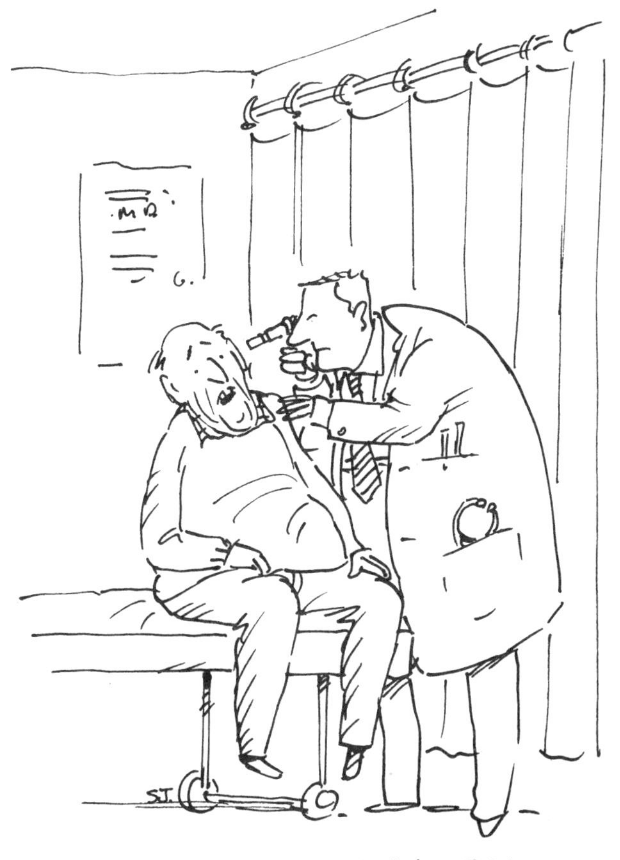

I WAS USING THIS TINY LITTLE MOBILE PHONE SEE... WHEN ALL OF A SUDDEN IT WENT RIGHT IN MY EAR

SO...YOU'VE DECIDED TO COME DOWN THEN?

I'M NOT SLEEPING WITH YOU LIKE THAT!
GO AND PUT SOME CLOTHES ON THIS MINUTE.

TESCO
M•S
SAINSBURY

CONSULTANT
BUT DOCTOR...AREN'T I THE ONE
WHO'S SUPPOSED TO UNDRESS

NEIGHBOURHOOD
WATCH AREA

HOLD YOUR HAND? WHAT ARE YOU SOME KIND OF SEX MANIAC?

A TIE.... OH YEAH, BLOODY THOUGHTFUL... THANKS

EITHER THIS BLOODY THING IS BUNGED UP...
OR YOU'RE DEAD

I'LL GET THOSE SLUGS
IF IT KILLS MEAAARGGH!!

FRANKLY I DON'T LIKE THE WAY THE FAMILY HAVE GATHERED AT THE BED-SIDE.

THIS IS MOTHER SUPERIOR –
WE CALL HER "NUN THE WISER"

ACCOUNTS
SLEEPING PARTNER
CHAIRMAN CHIEF EXEC:
SJ.

THE OLD ONES ARE THE BEST
SJ.

BLOODY HELL!
I'M EIGHTY YEARS OLD.
I WON'T MAKE THAT
MISTAKE AGAIN
HAPPY
BIRTHDAY

SJ.

STOP DANCING AROUND THE SUBJECT
... WHO IS SHE?

WELL I'M SORRY BUT IT'S THE BIGGEST ONE WE'VE GOT

AND IF YOU COME OUT OF RETIREMENT AGAIN - WE'LL TRY AND THINK OF SOMETHING DIFFERENT FOR YOU

YE GODS!
SHE USED TO BE MY
FAVOURITE FILM-STAR.
NOW SHE'S DOING DENTURE
CREAM COMMERCIALS
TV
S.J.

WHY ARE YOU SNIFFING
ICING-SUGAR UP YOUR NOSE DAD?

BY THE TIME YOU'VE TYPED THAT LAST WILL AND TESTAMENT YOU'LL BE DEAD AND BURIED

IF I LET GO
I'LL FALL DOWN WON'T I ?

SO WHAT'S THIS PROBLEM YOU'VE GOT WITH VIAGRA? ......AH!

YOU AND YOUR BLOODY DO-IT-YOURSELF

WHEN YOU'RE GOOD AND READY MISS...ER....

WELL-IT LOOKS LIKE A POUND-BUT WITH MY LUCK I'LL BEND OVER-BUGGER MY BACK AND FIND IT'S A PENNY
S.J.

YOU COULDN'T WAIT TO GET ME INTO BED COULD YOU?

YES COLONEL.. IT'S A MAGNIFICENT DECANTER....
BUT AN ORDINARY SAMPLE BOTTLE WOULD HAVE DONE

I KNOW I SAID "DON'T LOOK"
BUT YOU DON'T HAVE TO BE STUPID ABOUT IT

IF I DIDN'T KNOW ANY BETTER...
I'D SAY YOU ENJOY BEING A NAUGHTY BOY

WHAT EVER HAPPENED TO A GENTLEMAN OFFERING A LADY A SEAT?

YOU'VE GOT YOUR HAIR IN YOUR PORRIDGE OLD GIRL

YOU CAN MAKE YOUP POINT
WITHOUT USING YOUR WALKING STICK DAD

DON'T YOU LOVE ME ANYMORE?

HMMM... NICE....
BUT NOT QUITE THE WALKING SHOES I HAD IN MIND

WHEN YOU SUGGESTED BUYING SAUCY UNDERWEAR
O SPICE UP OUR SEX LIFE...I THOUGHT YOU MEANT FOR ME

JUST A PASSING SHOWER IS IT?

DOCTOR! MY NIPPLES HAVE COME OFF

I USE TO HAVE A GREAT NIGHT OUT AND FEEL LOUSY IN THE MORNING. NOW I JUST FEEL LOUSY IN THE MORNING
SJ

UP... UP... UP

...NO, WHEN I SAID "I CAN'T WAIT TO GET MY HEAD DOWN" I MEANT I CAN'T WAIT TO GET MY HEAD DOWN

AND WHO GOT OUT
OF THE WRONG SIDE OF THE BED
THIS MORNING ?

SJ

YOU'VE GONE OFF ME HAVEN'T YOU ?
YOU'RE WEARING A TRUSS

DO YOU WANT THESE... OR ARE YOU JUST GOING TO BRUSH YOUR GUMS TONIGHT?

WELL I'M VERY SORRY.....
BUT I DIDN'T DESIGN THE DOORWAY

I DON'T CARE WHERE WE SIT...
AS LONG AS IT'S NEAR A TOILET

HIS COLLAPSABLE STICK COLLAPSED

IT'S A LITTLE SOMETHING OF MY OWN...
3 PARTS WINCARNIS, 2 PARTS LIVER SALTS, ONE
PART STERADENT AND A DASH OF VIAGRA

NOW THAT'S HOW I LIKE 'EM....
PLENTY OF EXPERIENCE

... AND NO LOOKING UP MY NIGHTIE RIGHT?

A MAN WHO KNOWS WHAT HE LIKES

DO I TAKE IT THIS IS THE END OF OUR SEX LIFE?

WELL DOCTOR, I'VE GOT MEASLES, WHICH I CAUGHT
IN THE WAITING ROOM THE TIME I CAME IN WITH FLU
WHICH I CAUGHT WHEN I CAME IN FOR A CHECK-UP

RIGHT! I'M COMING TO BED NOW
AND I DON'T WANT ANY HANKY PANKY OKAY?

PENSIONERS SPECIAL LUNCH -
SALAD
FISH
MEAT
SWEETS
JELLY
KNIVES FORKS
SPOONS
TEETH
SJ.

DO YOU KNOW... I CAN'T REMEMBER
WHAT YOU LOOK LIKE FROM THE FRONT

WORST CASE OF PILES I'VE EVER SEEN

DID YOU MAKE THAT SNOWMAN HERBERT?

LET ME THROUGH... I'M A DOCTOR

OOOH! I JUST LOVE A MAN IN UNIFORM

YOU'VE GOT A PERFECTLY GOOD PAIR OF PYJAMA BOTTOMS... SO PUT THEM ON

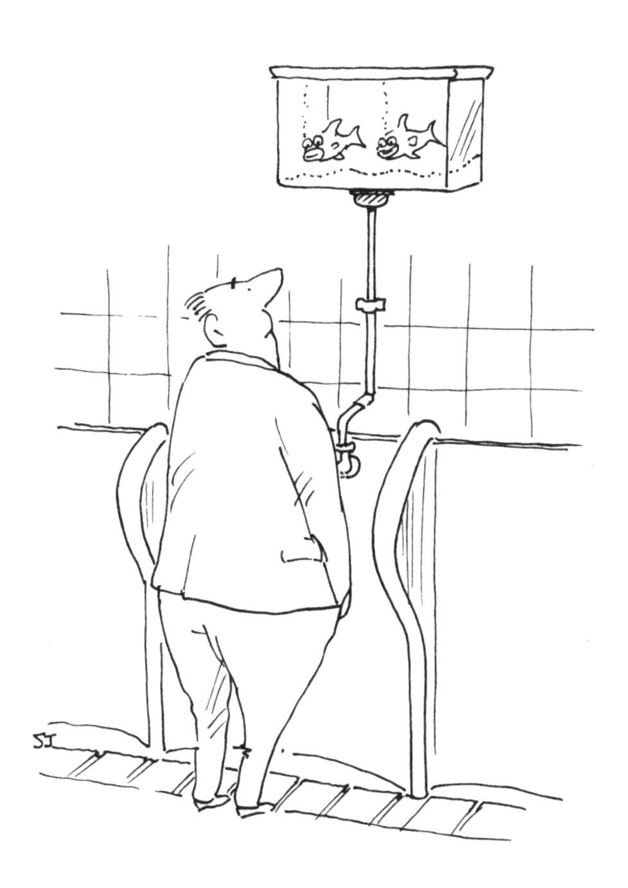
SJ

IT'S PROBABLY CALLED "A SECOND HONEYMOON"
BECAUSE IT'LL BE THE SECOND TIME WE'VE DONE IT.

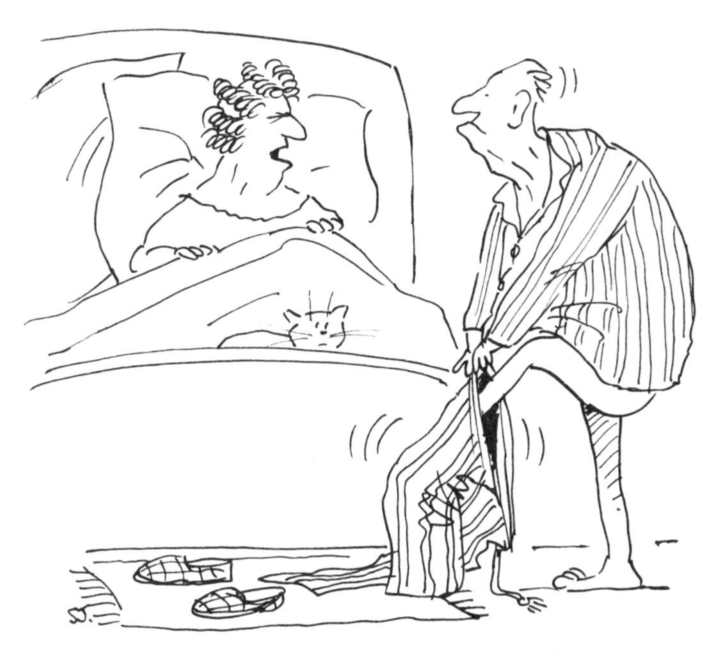

FORTUNATELY MY EYESIGHT IS
DETERIORATING AT THE SAME RATE AS YOUR BODY

NO, NO CYRIL....,
IT'S MUSIC TO GET YOU IN THE MOOD

I SUPPOSE THE BASTARD WAS LEGGING IT DOWN THE STAIRS WHILE I WAS COMING UP IN THE LIFT!

HE'S BEEN COMPLAINING
ABOUT PAINS IN HIS LEGS DOCTOR

YOU ALWAYS MANAGE
TO SPOIL THE MOOD DON'T YOU?

BUGGER!.. I USED TO FORGET TO DO MY FLIES UP.. THIS TIME I FORGOT TO UNDO THEM
S.J.

NO, NO, ...I SAID SIT!!

BUGGER!...I'VE DROPPED MY GLASSES

SEX SHOP
ADULT VIDEO'S
X VIDEO'S
ADULT BOOKS INSIDE
SEX TOYS

LATER!

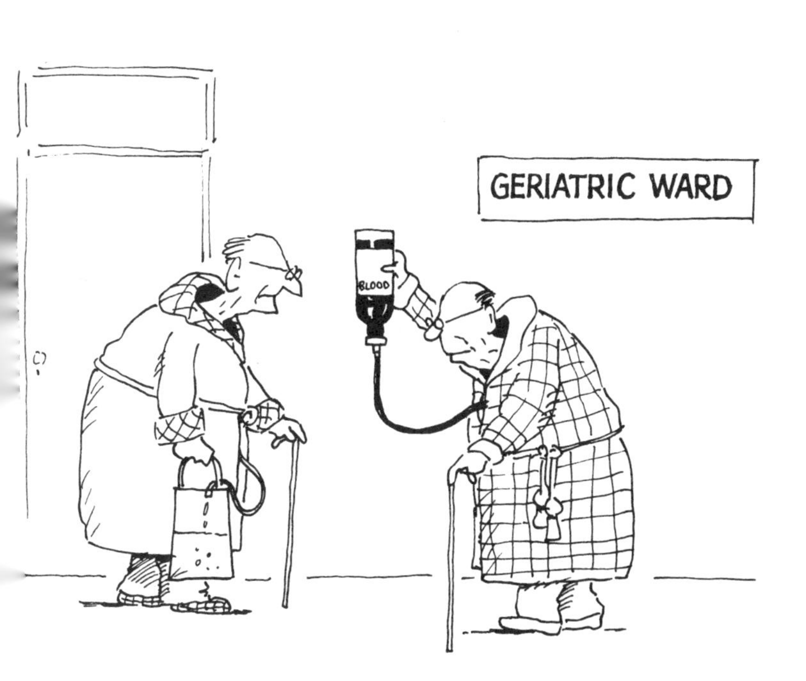
GERIATRIC WARD
BLOOD

... AND DON'T FORGET TO UNHOOK THE CAT

NOTICE HOW TIME FLIES WHETHER YOU'RE HAVING FUN OR NOT
SJ.

PERSONALLY, I'M MORE INTO RAP,
HIP HOP, GARAGE, ACID AND HARDHOUSE MYSELF

BETTER GO NOW DEAR, GEORGE HAS JUST DIED

HEY! THE MASK IS WORKING OLD GIRL...
I FELT A DEFINATE TWINGE

MY IDEA OF SAFE SEX, IS DOING IT
WITH SOMEONE WHO DOESNT HAVE A PACEMAKER

OLD PEOPLES HOME!

IF I'VE GOT TO HAVE WRINKLES-WHY CAN'T THEY BE ON THE SOLES OF MY FEET WHERE NOBODY SEES THEM
CREAM
SJ

CAN'T YOU THINK OF A NICER WAY
TO ENTERTAIN YOUR GRANDSON?

PHEW! PANT! PANT!.. THE OLDER I GET-
THE BETTER I USED TO BE.